For Mum and Bob, Dad and Maggie – M.G.

For Owen, Mum and Dad– H.A.

ACKNOWLEDGEMENTS
Tooth Ink and Fly Clashes first published in *The Scrumbler* Magazine, 2012
Rock Pool first published in *Poems About The Seaside* (Wayland, 2015)
Messages first published in *A Poem for Every Night of the Year* (Macmillan, 2016)
Fingerprints, Puzzle and Prayer first published in The Same Inside (Macmillan, 2018)

Chicken on the Roof

Poems by
Matt
Goodfellow

Illustrations by

Hannah Asen

Otter-Barry BOOKS

Contents

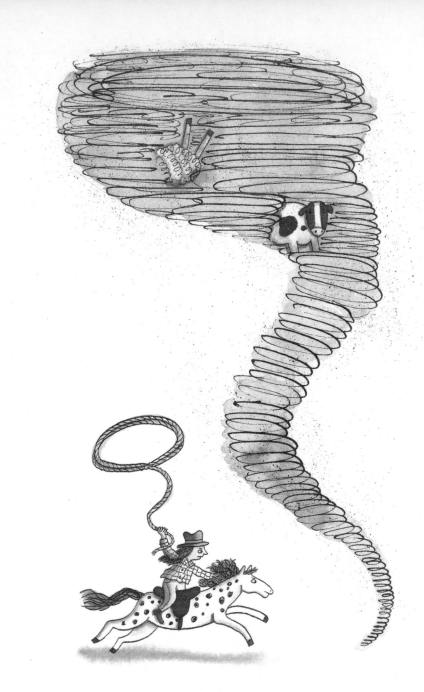

Heading Home

I fumbled through forests
wandered through waves
danced through the desert
and crawled into caves

cantered through canyons
squinted through squalls
raged across rivers
and wild waterfalls

carved through crevasses
conquered a cliff
tore through a twister
and marched through the mist

mastered the mountains
and sliced through the sea –
before I found out
I'd forgotten my key

Pop Group

The reason the group never made it?
Their career just seemed to be cursed....
Every time they walked onstage
the bassist promptly
BURST.

Can't I Please Just Stay in Bed?

(For Will)

Yes, I know the sun's shining
the sky is pure blue
and all of those things that you said
but my pillow's so comfy
I'm tired and grumpy
so can't I please just stay in bed?

I'm aware that it's lazy
I'm wasting the day
and I should be out playing instead
but the sun hurts my eyes
and I'm safer inside
so can't I please just stay in bed?

12

And what if a tiger
escapes from the zoo
and it's hungry and needs to be fed?
If I'm in the street he
will certainly eat me

so can't I please just stay in bed?

13

An Excellent Stick

a sorcerer's wand
for a magical trick
a mystical thing
is an excellent stick

a thunder-forged sword
victoriously quick
a glorious thing
is an excellent stick

a prize-winning rod
with a heave and a flick
a bountiful thing
is an excellent stick

a goalpost for saving
my brother's free-kick
a champion thing
is an excellent stick

it's mine and it's perfect
no other I'd pick
no game is the same
with an excellent stick

Why I Dislike Camping

Sleeping-bags make me anxious.

And I hate feeling tents.

Gone

She left last week for another school
somewhere out near Hartlepool.
I didn't cry, I played it cool –
now I wish I hadn't.

Deleted photos, mobile number,
left her standing there to wonder
why I slipped her arm and shunned her –
now I wish I hadn't.

They made her cards and sang a song.
I wouldn't, couldn't sing along.
Swallowed words, held my tongue –
how I wish I hadn't.

King of Birds

hide me from the lightning
little wren
rest inside your nest
up in the eaves

tonight I'll watch the sky
and hear you singing
and pray my proud protector
never leaves

*In folklore, some people believed that wrens' nests provided
protection against lightning. The wren was also known as
King of Birds.*

A Quiet Riot

A silent clash of titans
is taking place tonight.
We creep from under duvets
as Mum turns out the light....

We meet beneath the cabin bed,
a pillow in each hand,
the finest pair of warriors
to ever walk this land.

We fight a fevered contest,
fury in our eyes,
each gladiator struggling
to stifle battle cries

till footsteps on the landing
mean trouble's on the way....
Retreat, retreat, brave warrior –
and fight another day.

I'm Bored

dashboard
splashboard
seaboard
keyboard
backboard
blackboard
headboard
breadboard
scoreboard
floorboard
buckboard
duckboard
dartboard
SMARTboard
corkboard
chalkboard
springboard
stringboard
clipboard
chipboard
billboard

I'm
STILL
bored!

Fly Clashes

At the funeral of the fly
I couldn't help but cry.
And the reason why?
It was in my eye.

Everything Passes
(for Rachel Rooney)

the end of a storm
like a rag on a thorn

a shoot in the mud
like a blossoming bud

the dawn in the skies
like the sap on the rise

the sea in a shell
like a wish in a well

a kiss in the dark
like a coin in the bark

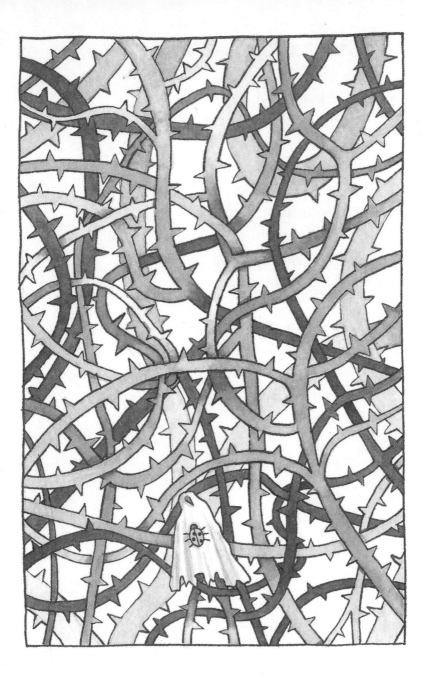

What a Day!

What a day!
Fell asleep on a bench,
when I woke up
I was speaking French.

What a day!
Mum's nose turned purple,
Dad found the square root
of a circle.

What a day!
Gran lost her grin,
spat her false teeth
in the kitchen bin.

What a day!
I had school dinner,
ate ten burgers
yet I'm slightly thinner.

What a day!
Misplaced my shoe,
my trousers turned
to superglue.

What a day!
The cat went weird,
did its business
in Grandpa's beard.

"What a day!"
is what I said,
now thank the stars
it's time for bed.

Growing Home

the seed we found
and placed in the ground
that night when life
went wild

it grew and grew
and me and you
watched it grow
and smiled

it grew so far
it touched the stars
which told us
it was time

to leave this town
and not look down
and climb
and climb

and climb

Haiku

in morning's frost-glass
a slice of lunar lemon –
the last twist of night

Ptarmigan

A ptarmigan's cardigan's
perfect in the snow:
soft, warm, beautiful,
then – *blink* – where'd he go?

A ptarmigan (pronounced TARmigan) is a plump gamebird. In winter, it becomes completely white except for small patches on its eyes and tail. It breeds in the highest mountains of the Scottish Highlands.

Fit

every pan needs a lid
every bus needs a stop
every bike needs a wheel
every drip needs a drop

every toe needs a heel
every sole needs a shoe
every day needs a dream
every me needs a you

33

Messages

look closely and you'll find them
everywhere

in fields of patterned grasses
drafted by the hare

embroidered by the bluebells
through a wood

in scattered trails of blossom
stamped into the mud

scorched by heather-fire
across the moors

in looping snail-trails
scrawled on forest floors

scored across the sky
by screaming swifts

in rolling, twisting peaks
of drifting mountain mist

scribbled by an ocean
on the sand

look closely: you will see
and understand

Why I Should Probably Avoid Dancing in my Room From Now On

I waltzed with abandon
and tangoed with feeling
then cartwheeled commandingly

straight through the ceiling

Library Poem

Stride inside a library,
find yourself a book,
dive between the pages
in a comfy cosy nook.

Travel distant places,
ride a unicorn.
Hide in deepest outer space
before the Earth was born.

Sail off in an air-balloon
to skies of purest blue.
Learn about the llamas
that you laughed at in the zoo.

Climb a crystal glacier,
meet a mighty king.
Slide into a silent sea
where mermaids softly sing.

A library will guide you,
show you what to do.
So stride inside a library –
the library needs you too.

Rock Pool

Barnacle's on bass guitar,
hermit-crab's on drums,
starfish does the singing
and a shrimp guitarist strums.

The hardest rockin' group around,
come catch us, playing live –
but get your ticket quick because
we tour with every tide!

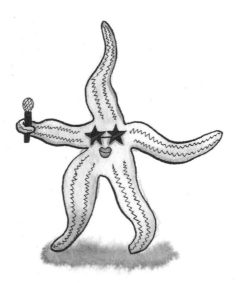

Hide and Seek

(by Matt and Daisy Goodfellow)

hide in the butter
hide in a tree
hide in the nest
of a big bumblebee

hide in a teapot
hide in a drawer
hide in the teeth
of a crocodile's jaw

hide in a slipper
hide in a shoe
hide in a bottle
of PVA glue

hide in a mattress
hide in the sink
hide in the fizz
of your big brother's drink

hide in a beanbag
hide in a pram
hide in a jar
of raspberry jam

hide in the toilet
hide in a coat
hide in the hair
of an African goat

hide in the toothpaste
hide in a ball
hide in the cracks
of an old garden wall

hide in the flannel
hide in the snow
I can still find you
wherever you go

Little Boat

little boat
on the sea
bobs about
waves at me

yellow sail
silver sway
little boat
drifts away

Where Our School Used to Be

When the wrecking balls had stopped
we stood at the gate to see
mud and broken bricks
and a space where our school used to be.

The old one was *fraught with danger,*
said the man from the powers that be.
So they built a new one far away
from the space where our school used to be.

The only thing left standing
was the ancient sycamore tree –
no jumpers are scattered beneath it
in the space where our school used to be.

But when we're here together,
Archie, Cain and me,
we still hear the laughter
in the space where our school used to be.

Advice

My tip
for climbing
Everest?

Keep
on going.
Never rest.

Before

before the tree
the seed
before the bread
the knead
before the end
the start
before the break
the heart
before the low
the high
before the fail
the try
before the heal
the sore
before the drink
the pour
before the sun
the cream
before the wake
the dream

Tooth Ink

Tooth ink is special
tooth ink is bright
tooth ink of you
fills my pen with delight!

From the Land to the Sea

For eternity
she casts her wedding veil
across my sands,
then glides to the horizon,
trailing twists of silken strands.

But here I stand so faithfully
in wait for time and tide,
for one day when the stars were young
she became my bride.

Yo-Yo Poem

My Loop the Loop is legendary,
Walk the Dog's a stroll.
I'm rather good at Robin Hood,
unmatched at Barrel Roll.

I Split the Atom smoothly.
Reverse Trapeze? A breeze.
My Eiffel Tower's excellent,
I Waterfall with ease.

My talent is unparalleled,
a fearless, peerless swinger.
The only trick I need to learn –
removing it from my finger.

Tracks

Tracks in the snow
are crunchy and new.

Tracks in the grass
sparkle with dew.

Tracks in the mud
are gloopy like glue.

Tracks in cement:
'Oiiiiiiiiii, YOU!!!'

I Was Born a Unicorn

I can ride the light of dawn
I was born a unicorn
somewhere deep within a storm
I was born a unicorn

Cast away convention,
imagination flows.
Follow me and destiny
along another road.

I can ride the light of dawn
I was born a unicorn
somewhere deep within a storm
I was born a unicorn

Free from worldly worry,
starting to transform.
Leave behind the shallow grind
of things you mustn't mourn.

I can ride the light of dawn
I was born a unicorn
somewhere deep within a storm
I was born a unicorn

Become the rolling rhythm
of thunder through the sky.
Hoof and horn replace all scorn
forever, you and I.

you can ride the light of dawn
you were born a unicorn
somewhere deep within a storm
you were born a unicorn

Fingerprints

I try to find where mine
begin and end.

Frustratedly, I check
those of my friend.

She watches, gentle-eyed
and starts to speak:

*Don't try to understand
what is unique.*

Hug

a hug is hello
a hug is goodbye

a hug is it's over
a hug is let's try

a hug is I'm sorry
a hug is well done

a hug is you lost
a hug is you won

a hug is I'll help you
escape any fear

a hug is I love you
I'll always be here

Tommy's Tummy

Tommy ate the table,
Tommy ate the chair,
Tommy ate the cushions
that were scattered everywhere.

Tommy ate the TV,
Tommy ate the cat,
Tommy ate the little gnome
that lived outside our flat.

Tommy ate the toaster,
Tommy ate the car,
Tommy ate the neck
and all the strings of my guitar.

Tommy ate the trophy
that stood upon his shelf,
then Tommy sighed, unsatisfied,
and Tommy ate himself.

The Salt-Maker's Song

In the shadow of Snowdon
I sing of white gold
where mussel-shells cobble the shore.

Each note on the staves
of the cold Menai waves
is crystalline, perfect and pure.

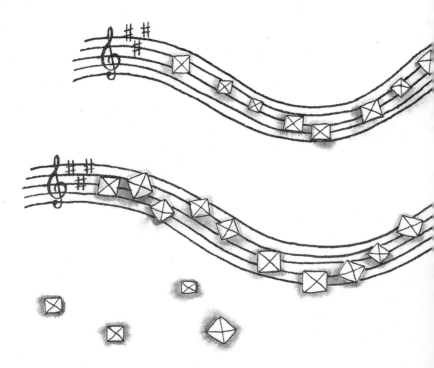

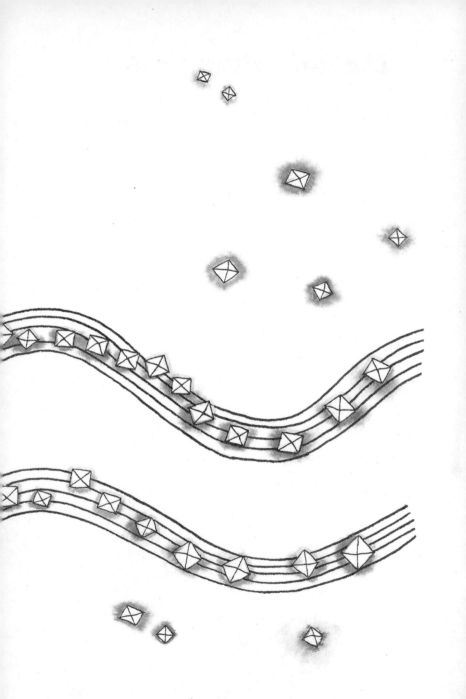

Chicken on the Roof

there's a chicken
there's a chicken
there's a chicken on the roof

I ain't telling you no lies, man, I'm telling you the truth!

there's a chicken
there's a chicken
there's a chicken on the roof

I've absolutely no idea why she's flown the coop!

there's a chicken
there's a chicken
there's a chicken on the roof

Someone find a recipe for spicy chicken soup!

there's a chicken
there's a chicken
there's a chicken on the roof

If I was Australian the word I'd use is *strewth*!

there's a chicken
there's a chicken
there's a chicken on the roof

The only way she's coming down is chicken parachute!

there's a chicken
there's a chicken
there's a chicken on the roof

This is a true story: there really was a chicken on my roof, called Sage. She flew in from a neighbour's garden. Eventually she did manage to fly down, after a couple of days looking dejected!

Still There

I see you near the river,
half-extinguished by the mist.

I see you in the summer fields
where dandelions drift.

I see you through the stubble-plains,
autumn at your back.

I see you on the skyline
when night is winter-black.

I follow you down shadow-lanes
where memories still pass.

I walk within your footsteps,
haloed in the morning grass.

65

Tin Talk

I talk with my tin,
my aluminium twin,
about all of the things
that we keep deep within.

We talk about futures,
we talk about dreams.
But mainly, it seems,
we talk about beans.

Greedy-Guts Goliath

I'm Greedy-Guts Goliath and I'm coming to your
street.
I'm going to steal the things you like, the things you
love to eat.
I'm going to steal your sausages, your crisps and
sticky jam,
I'm going to steal your caramels, your cream and
coq au vin.

I'm going to steal your Battenberg, your *bhajis* and
your *bagel.*
I'm going to steal the *poppadoms* that tower on your
table.
I'm going to steal your *cullen skink*, your bubble and
your squeak,
I'm going to steal your *pitta* bread, your pepper and
your leek.

I'm going to steal your jellied eel and toad that's in
its hole.
I'm going to steal your sweetcorn soup, your cracker
and spring roll.
I'm going to steal your broccoli, your slow-cooked
chicken stew
and when I've eaten what I want, I'll probably eat –

YOU!

The Madness of the Moors

Blistered in the distance,
staring at the moon,
stumbling together
they gather in the gloom.

Scattered on the black hills,
peat-bog-painted pores,
in clouded eyes you recognise
the madness of the moors.

A thousand shifting shadows,
they spill across the night,
reaching from the recesses
towards the village lights.

So clutch your rowan crosses,
lay blossom at your doors
and pray that they can save you from
the madness of the moors.

A Hedgehog's Swimming Report

Front-crawl: good
Back-stroke: painful

Prayer

I'm never too busy for fairy tales,
I'm never too busy for games,
I'm never too busy for singing a song
or making a den when it rains.

I'm never too busy for rainbows,
I'm never too busy for dreams,
I'm never too busy for frightening friends
and filling a room with their screams.

I'm never too busy for birthdays,
I'm never too busy to cry,
I'm never too busy to stare at the stars
that glitter a clear summer sky.

I'm never too busy for sprinkles
or chocolate ice-cream after tea,
I'm never too busy to say what I think.
Please, Lord, say I never will be.

Storm Clouds

Rumbling bombers
in from the sea
carry a furious thunder decree:

We are the power. This is the law.
Welcome the darkness. Black to the core.

Shattering shorelines. Splintering sand.

Now

now

we take the land.

Cousins

cousin Tim
massive grin

cousin Rose
picks her nose

cousin Steve
dirty knees

cousin Nina
such a dreamer

cousin Bertie
getting shirty

cousin Sita
noisy eater

cousin Paul
rather tall

cousin Flora
sofa-snorer

cousin Sal
my best pal

cousin Claire
crazy hair

cousins cousins
everywhere

Puzzle

we are
all
jigsaw pieces

before
we
are gone

we
must
find
a way

to
fit
together
as

one

Natural Historian's Reunion

Agatha liked aardvarks
Denzel adored deer
Ken was keen on crocodiles
(so sad he can't be here)

The Children of the Hum

we are the children
of the hum
receivers of its song
melodies like mercury
still keep us marching strong

Where skylines buzz with charging chime
each impulse is an order.
We live to give them what they want,
existing on the border

of spaces people never see,
with those who recognise
this symphony of synergy
is where the power lies.

we are the children
of the hum
receivers of its song
melodies like mercury
still keep us marching strong

Others says we're in a trance,
crazy pylon people,
but we have seen the crackle-dance
beneath each metal steeple.

We move and flow like energy,
thin and wild and free,
explore the urge, become the surge
and listen carefully.

we are the children
of the hum
receivers of its song
melodies like mercury
still keep us marching strong

Weird History

Famous French monarch Louis XIV
was known as the Sun King

yet

he reigned for 72 years.

Walk

the mown path
through the park
sparkles with dew
which stains the tips
of these too-tight shoes
and way way up
in the stillness
of the blue
passengers
sip cardboard teas
suck boiled sweets
lean back in their seats
and know nothing
of me
down here
on my last walk
to school

Quick

I'm stuck inside a crossword,
I don't know what to do.
I'll never find the answer
when I haven't got a clue.

Off

off the beach
off the hook
off the rim
off the cuff

off the grid
off the edge
off the shelf
off the peg

off the boil
off the scale
off the wall
off the rails

off the record
off the stage
off the telly

off

        the

                p

                a

Gobbling Goblins

Gobbling goblins
scream and spit,
slobber and slather
and smack their lips,

squabble and snatch
and pick black teeth,
lick dirty fingers
and stuff green cheeks,

argue and shout
when their mouths are full,
snap and steal
and tear and pull,

86

never say thank you,
don't even care,
smash up all the crockery
and dribble everywhere,

elbow everybody
as they swallow and slurp –
and finish every meal
with a table-shaking

BURP!

Miss Bouquet's End-of-Year Class Comments

Lily: Somewhat sombre. Rarely smiles.

Blossom: Flighty. Scatty. Can't sit still.

Heather: Rugged outdoors type. A survivor.

Poppy: Respectful. Excellent memory. A great example to others.

Holly: Difficult to handle. Prickly.

Ivy: Takes over. Always where she shouldn't be.

Daisy: A daydreamer. Sun-chaser. Stares out of the window all day.

Lavender: A gentle child – a nice calming influence.

Palmela: Thinks she's something she's not.

My Nose

my nose
is a forward-thinker

my nose
is straight down the middle

my nose
has got its head screwed on the right way

my nose
knows

Rain Snake

The
     rain snake

         on my

            window

               glistens

                  as it glides

                     through

                  the swollen

                    droplets

                    with

                  sun-spots

            in its eyes

The Green Man's Child

The moon is a coin in night's deep river
when a voice calls me out from my bed,

down the old mill path, through the field to
    the woods
with the words of the wind in my head.

Caressed by a mist hanging low through the trees
by the edge of a star-swell stream,

every sound from the shadows is a song in my veins,
each footstep a place I have been.

At the base of an oak in a long brown cloak
sits a man I have always known.

Carved on his face is a wild-storm grace:
"You were called, you have come. You are home."

He speaks through his beard in a voice low and clear and his eyes meet mine and he smiles.

*"The woods and streams are a part of your dreams,
for you are the Green Man's child."*

The Green Man has been mentioned throughout history for thousands of years. In pre-Christian religions, trees were sacred and forests were thought to hold ghosts and nature spirits. The Green Man is often depicted as a man's face covered in leaves. He is often associated with spring and is a central figure in May Day celebrations.

Slip Away

I took the air at the seaside
home inside a jar,
safe within a rucksack
in the boot of Grandma's car.
Every now and then
I slowly twist the lid
and savour scented memories
of seaside things we did.

I caught the morning sunlight
on both my shining cheeks,
carried it away with me
and warmed myself for weeks.
And as the sunlight faded
I gave a gentle sigh
and watched the summer drift away –
goodbye goodbye goodbye.

I stole a quiet moment,
kept it for myself,
hidden in my bedroom
high upon a shelf.
And when the world is noisy
and madness fills the day,
I'll lift the lid on what I hid
and softly slip away.

About the Poet and the Illustrator

Matt Goodfellow is a poet and primary school teacher from Manchester. Hailed in Poetry Zone as a *"fresh, young and welcome new voice to children's poetry"*, this is his second collection of poems, following *Carry Me Away*. Since embarking on his poetry career, Matt's high-energy poetry performances and workshops have delighted and enthused thousands of children across the UK.

If you would like Matt to visit your school, library or book festival, please contact him at **mattgoodfellowpoet@hotmail.com** or on Twitter: @EarlyTrain

Hannah Asen creates vibrant pen-and-ink illustrations fuelled with humour and imagination. She studied art and languages at Edinburgh University before relocating to Berlin in 2010. In 2017 Hannah returned to the UK and now lives in Edinburgh, where her studio is filled with inks, paints and characters, all coming to life.

www.hannahasen.com